MW00610502

GREAT MINDS® WIT & WISDOM

Grade K Module 4:
The Continents

Student Edition

COPYRIGHT STATEMENT

Published by Great Minds®.

ISBN: 978-1-68386-020-4

Table of Contents

Name: _____

Handout 8A: Passport Journal

Directions: Write your name and home continent on the lines provided on page 1. On pages 2–8, draw and label one detail about the continent pictured in the top right corner.

Student Picture

Name: _____

Continent: _____

Handout 8A: Passport Journal

Europe

Name:

Handout 8A: Passport Journal

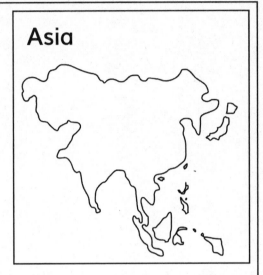

Asia

Handout 8A: Passport Journal

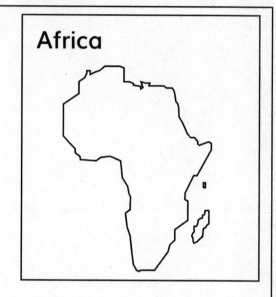

Africa

Name:

Handout 8A: Passport Journal

Antarctica

Handout 8A: Passport Journal

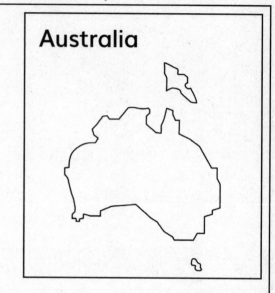

Australia

Name: _____

Handout 8A: Passport Journal

South America

Handout 8A: Passport Journal

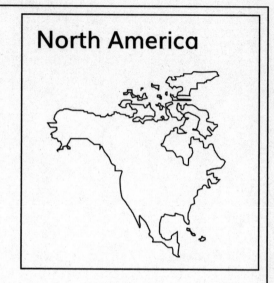

North America

Name:

Handout 9A: Opposite Describing Words

Directions: Draw a line between opposite describing words.

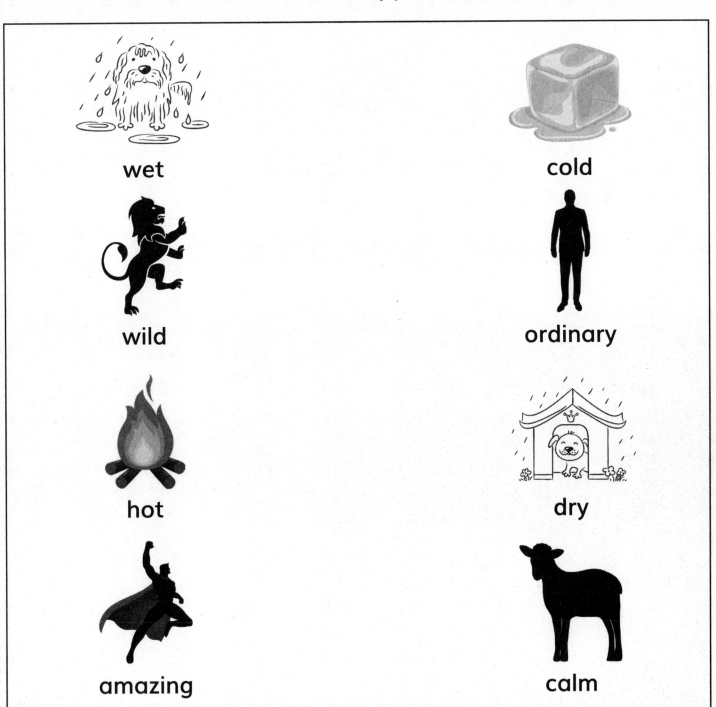

wet

cold

wild

ordinary

hot

dry

amazing

calm

Name: _____

Handout 21A: Sentence Expansion

Directions: In the top box, draw a picture of an animal from the story. In the middle box, write a complete sentence. Tell the animal's name and what it is doing. In the bottom box, expand the sentence by adding a describing word and telling where or when it happened.

Name:

Handout 31A: Natural Features Map

Directions: Draw a line from each natural feature to its label. Each label has two natural feature matches.

Mount McKinley

mountain

Great Lakes

Hudson River

river

Mojave Desert

Rocky Mountains

desert

Everglades

Arizona Desert

lake

Mississippi River

Name: _____

Handout 32A: Sentence Improvement

Part 1 Directions: On the first line, answer "Who?" by writing an animal name. On the second line, tell what the animal is doing. On the third line, write the complete sentence.

Who?_____

Does What?_____

Complete Sentence: _____

_____

Part 2 Directions: Improve your complete sentence. Begin your sentence with a capital letter. Expand your sentence by adding a describing word or telling where or when your sentence happened. Decide if your sentence is a telling sentence, a loud and exciting sentence, or an asking sentence. End your sentence with the correct punctuation mark.

Name:

Handout 34A: End-of-Module Task Checklist

Directions: Circle 🙂 Yes or 😐 Not Yet to answer each prompt.

Reading Comprehension	Self		Peer		Teacher	
I used words to find evidence about the continents.	🙂 Yes	😐 Not Yet	🙂 Yes	😐 Not Yet	🙂 Yes	😐 Not Yet
I used illustrations to find evidence about the continents.	🙂 Yes	😐 Not Yet	🙂 Yes	😐 Not Yet	🙂 Yes	😐 Not Yet
Structure	Self		Peer		Teacher	
I wrote an opinion statement.	🙂 Yes	😐 Not Yet	🙂 Yes	😐 Not Yet	🙂 Yes	😐 Not Yet
I wrote two supporting reason sentences for my opinion.	🙂 Yes	😐 Not Yet	🙂 Yes	😐 Not Yet	🙂 Yes	😐 Not Yet
I wrote an opinion conclusion by stating my opinion again.	🙂 Yes	😐 Not Yet	🙂 Yes	😐 Not Yet	🙂 Yes	😐 Not Yet

Style	Self		Peer		Teacher	
I drew pictures to add information to my travel brochure.	☺ Yes	😐 Not Yet	☺ Yes	😐 Not Yet	☺ Yes	😐 Not Yet
Conventions	**Self**		**Peer**		**Teacher**	
I used capital letters at the beginning of sentences. ABC	☺ Yes	😐 Not Yet	☺ Yes	😐 Not Yet	☺ Yes	😐 Not Yet
I wrote complete sentences that tell "who, did what."	☺ Yes	😐 Not Yet	☺ Yes	😐 Not Yet	☺ Yes	😐 Not Yet
Total number of ☺						

Volume of Reading Reflection Questions

The Continents, Kindergarten, Module 4

Student Name:

Text:

Author:

Topic:

Genre/type of book:

After reading your book, share what you learned. Draw a picture or tell your teacher your answer to each question.

Informational Text

1. **Wonder:** What do you notice about this book from the front and back cover of the book? What questions do you have about this book?

2. **Organize:** What main ideas are discussed in this book? Point to the key details that you noticed.

3. **Reveal:** What information in this text is similar to information learned in a class text? Point to the part of the book that has similar information. How is the information different from our class text?

4. **Distill:** What big idea did the author want you to learn about in this book?

5. **Know:** What new information do you now know about other continents or countries? Share the new information that you learned.

6. **Vocabulary:** Find two words in the text that have opposites. Act out the word in the text and its opposite. (For example, if *huge* is in the text, act out both the words *huge* and *tiny*.)

Literary Text

1. Wonder: What are you noticing in this story?

2. Organize: What happens in this story? Tell how the illustrations help to add important details to the story.

3. Reveal: Illustrations help to fill in more details in stories. Tell how an illustration adds details to the setting of this story.

4. Distill: Do any of the characters in this story learn a lesson? What lesson do they learn? Is it a lesson you could use in your life today?

5. Know: What have you learned about life in other places by reading this book?

6. Vocabulary: Find an illustration that helps you to understand a word that was new to you. Draw the object and tell how the illustration helped you.

WIT & WISDOM PARENT TIP SHEET

WHAT IS MY KINDERGARTEN STUDENT LEARNING IN MODULE 4?

Wit & Wisdom is our English curriculum. It builds knowledge of key topics in history, science, and literature through the study of excellent texts. By reading and responding to stories and nonfiction texts, we will build knowledge of the following topics:

Module 1: The Five Senses

Module 2: Once Upon a Farm

Module 3: America, Then and Now

Module 4: The Continents

In the fourth module, *The Continents*, we will study characteristics of the seven continents to learn more about the world and understand the similarities and differences amongst the continents. As we explore each continent, we ask the question: *What makes the world fascinating?*

OUR CLASS WILL READ THESE BOOKS:

Picture Books (Informational)

- *Africa*, Rebecca Hirsch
- *Antarctica*, Rebecca Hirsch
- *Asia*, Rebecca Hirsch
- *Australia*, Rebecca Hirsch
- *Europe*, Rebecca Hirsch
- *Introducing North America*, Chris Oxlade
- *South America*, Rebecca Hirsch
- *World Atlas*, Nick Crane

Picture Books (Literary)

- *Moon Rope*, Lois Ehlert
- *The Story of Ferdinand*, Munro Leaf
- *Why Mosquitoes Buzz in People's Ears: A West African Tale*, Verna Aardema

OUR CLASS WILL READ THIS ARTICLE:

- "5 Reasons Why Animal Moms Are Awesome," April Capochino Myers

OUR CLASS WILL EXAMINE THIS PAINTING:

- *Carta Marina*, Olaus Magnus

OUR CLASS WILL VISIT THIS WEB PAGE:

- "Americas—Fact Files," *Go Wild*

OUR CLASS WILL READ THIS POEM:

- "Lions Roar," *CanTeach*

OUR CLASS WILL LISTEN TO THESE SONGS

- "Penguin Song," *Preschool Education*
- "*Where in the World Is Carmen Sandiego?* from Smithsonian Folkways" Smithsonian Folkways

OUR CLASS WILL WATCH THESE VIDEOS:

- "Antarctic Sights and Sounds," James Napoli
- "Burkina Faso: Music," *Our Africa*
- "Explore Views of the Burj Khalifa with Google Maps," Google Maps
- "The Seven Continents Song," Silly School Songs
- "Storm-Proofing the World's Biggest Mud Building," BBC Earth
- "Traditional Chinese Dance—'Flowers Contend in Beauty' by Li Qian, Lin Chen..."

OUR CLASS WILL VIEW THESE PHOTOGRAPHS

- *Earth from Space*, Stöckli, Reto, et al.
- "Patterns of Chinchero," *Descendants of the Incas*

OUR CLASS WILL ASK THESE QUESTIONS:

- What interesting things can people do in Europe and Asia?
- What interesting natural features can people see in Africa and Antarctica?
- How can a story transport you to a different place?
- What amazing animals can people see in South America and Australia?
- Why might people want to visit North America?

QUESTIONS TO ASK AT HOME:

As you read with your Kindergarten student, ask:

- How does this text build your knowledge of the continents? Share what you know about the continents.

BOOKS TO READ AT HOME:

- *Koala Lou*, Mem Fox
- *Ganesha's Sweet Tooth*, Emily Haynes and Sanjay Patel
- *Life Story*, Virginia Lee Burton
- *Animal Architects: Amazing Animals Who Build Their Homes*, Daniel Nasser and Julio Antonio Blasco
- *Follow the Dream: The Story of Christopher Columbus*, Peter Sís
- *Tikki Tikki Tembo*, Arlene Mosel
- *The Barefoot Book of Animal Tales*, Naomi Adler
- *Introducing Antartica*, Anita Ganeri
- *Introducing Asia*, Anita Ganeri
- *Introducing Australia*, Anita Ganeri
- *Emmanuel's Dream: The True Story of Emmanuel Ofosu Yeboah*, Laurie Ann Thompson
- *Wee Gillis*, Munro Leaf
- *Charles Darwin's Around-the-World Adventure*, Jennifer Thermes

PLACES YOU CAN VISIT TO TALK ABOUT THE WORLD:

Visit a natural history museum and circulate through aspects of different cultures and continents. Ask:

- What do you notice and wonder about the animals, art, and artifacts of this continent?
- How does life in this place seem similar to and different from your life?
- Imagine visiting this place in person. What might you do if you went there? What things would you like to see? What animals would you like to see? What questions do you have about this place?

CREDITS

Great Minds® has made every effort to obtain permission for the reprinting of all copyrighted material. If any owner of copyrighted material is not acknowledged herein, please contact Great Minds® for proper acknowledgment in all future editions and reprints of this module.

- All material from the *Common Core State Standards for English Language Arts & Literacy in History/Social Studies, Science, and Technical Subjects* © Copyright 2010 National Governors Association Center for Best Practices and Council of Chief State School Officers. All rights reserved.

- All images are used under license from Shutterstock.com unless otherwise noted.

- For updated credit information, please visit **http://witeng.link/credits**.

ACKNOWLEDGMENTS

Great Minds® Staff

The following writers, editors, reviewers, and support staff contributed to the development of this curriculum.

Ann Brigham, Lauren Chapalee, Sara Clarke, Emily Climer, Lorraine Griffith, Emily Gula, Sarah Henchey, Trish Huerster, Stephanie Kane-Mainier, Lior Klirs, Liz Manolis, Andrea Minich, Lynne Munson, Marya Myers, Rachel Rooney, Aaron Schifrin, Danielle Shylit, Rachel Stack, Sarah Turnage, Michelle Warner, Amy Wierzbicki, Margaret Wilson, and Sarah Woodard.

Colleagues and Contributors

We are grateful for the many educators, writers, and subject-matter experts who made this program possible.

David Abel, Robin Agurkis, Elizabeth Bailey, Julianne Barto, Amy Benjamin, Andrew Biemiller, Charlotte Boucher, Sheila Byrd-Carmichael, Eric Carey, Jessica Carloni, Janine Cody, Rebecca Cohen, Elaine Collins, Tequila Cornelious, Beverly Davis, Matt Davis, Thomas Easterling, Jeanette Edelstein, Kristy Ellis, Moira Clarkin Evans, Charles Fischer, Marty Gephart, Kath Gibbs, Natalie Goldstein, Christina Gonzalez, Mamie Goodson, Nora Graham, Lindsay Griffith, Brenna Haffner, Joanna Hawkins, Elizabeth Haydel, Steve Hettleman, Cara Hoppe, Ashley Hymel, Carol Jago, Jennifer Johnson, Mason Judy, Gail Kearns, Shelly Knupp, Sarah Kushner, Shannon Last, Suzanne Lauchaire, Diana Leddy, David Liben, Farren Liben, Jennifer Marin, Susannah Maynard, Cathy McGath, Emily McKean, Jane Miller, Rebecca Moore, Cathy Newton, Turi Nilsson, Julie Norris, Galemarie Ola, Michelle Palmieri, Meredith Phillips, Shilpa Raman, Tonya Romayne, Emmet Rosenfeld, Jennifer Ruppel, Mike Russoniello, Deborah Samley, Casey Schultz, Renee Simpson, Rebecca Sklepovich, Amelia Swabb, Kim Taylor, Vicki Taylor, Melissa Thomson, Lindsay Tomlinson, Melissa Vail, Keenan Walsh, Julia Wasson, Lynn Welch, Yvonne Guerrero Welch, Emily Whyte, Lynn Woods, and Rachel Zindler.

Early Adopters

The following early adopters provided invaluable insight and guidance for Wit & Wisdom:

- Bourbonnais School District 53 • Bourbonnais, IL
- Coney Island Prep Middle School • Brooklyn, NY
- Gate City Charter School for the Arts • Merrimack, NH
- Hebrew Academy for Special Children • Brooklyn, NY
- Paris Independent Schools • Paris, KY
- Saydel Community School District • Saydel, IA
- Strive Collegiate Academy • Nashville, TN
- Valiente College Preparatory Charter School • South Gate, CA
- Voyageur Academy • Detroit, MI

Design Direction provided by Alton Creative, Inc.

Project management support, production design, and copyediting services provided by **ScribeConcepts.com**

Copyediting services provided by Fine Lines Editing

Product management support provided by Sandhill Consulting